COLLEGE LONDON PRESS

C000261898

GRADE

07

PIANO

**12 pieces plus exercises for
Trinity College London
exams 2021-2023**
Now with performance notes

Published by
Trinity College London Press Ltd
trinitycollege.com

Registered in England
Company no. 09726123

Cover photograph courtesy of Steinway & Sons

Printed in England by Caligraving Ltd

Performance notes

Invention no. 12 in A major / J S Bach — Page 6

▶ Baroque
▶ Independence of hands
▶ Variety of articulation

Johann Sebastian Bach's set of 15 two-part 'Inventions' were written for his son, Wilhelm Friedemann, as part of his education at the keyboard. They are designed to develop complete independence of the hands, with each part being an equal partner in the musical conversation.

The A major 'Invention' is a lively, upbeat piece, where the moderate dotted-crotchet pulse is hidden under a constant web of semiquavers, with crochets and longer notes frequently ornamented. Although there are no performance markings in the score, you might like to add some dynamic variation of your own, and certainly a degree of variation in the articulation. With dynamics, many of these might be relatively small-scale, lightening one hand and emphasising the other to give precedence to the thematic material.

With articulation, you might like to think of string players – as Bach himself was. In particular, imagine how a bow might be used to join some notes together and separate others. Even better, watch a violinist or cellist playing some of Bach's solo works for those instruments. The most important thing is to bring the music to life with whatever articulation you decide on – perhaps think of it as bringing light and shade into a picture.

Although Bach played one of the earliest models of fortepiano, performing his keyboard works on the modern piano has always resulted in a huge variety of performance styles, so it's well worth seeking out a number of recordings by different pianists for comparison.

Capriccio in G minor / Handel — Page 8

▶ Baroque
▶ Contrapuntal
▶ Articulation

'Capriccio' is a title that has been used in an enormous number of different ways in music, with the only common thread being a lively, fast-paced and often virtuosic character.

This 'Capriccio' contains some strict imitative writing, which gives the piece a restless feel, rather like one hand is chasing the other. With this in mind, the way you play the opening four bars sets an important precedent for the rest of the piece, particularly in terms of the articulation. You might like to think of the arpeggiated quavers as slightly detached, whereas the semiquaver scale figures might be more *legato*. There are plenty of different options: take bar 4 as an example. You might prefer to pair the semiquavers in the first part of the bar, as if they were slurred. You could continue this into the second half of the bar, perhaps slurring the first two of each set of four semiquavers. Equally, you

might decide to detach the semiquavers in the first half of the bar, to give a crisper feel to the music. Either way, try to copy any articulation from this passage when it occurs later on in the piece – in the left or right hand, or (as in bar 12) both hands at the same time!

In the last section, from bar 27, notice how this starts with a semiquaver rest in the right hand, as if there were a breath marked for a woodwind or brass player. In the bars that follow, you might like to follow this same idea, taking an imaginary breath after the first semiquaver of the bar. This is both a musical consideration to point out the phrasing, but also a technical one, giving you time to make the often-sizeable jump to the second semiquaver of the bar!

Handel would have played this piece on a harpsichord, and it's worth finding a recording performed on one to get a feel for the energetic character of the music.

Finale / Haydn — Page 11

▶ Classical
▶ Variations
▶ Syncopation

This joyful concluding movement takes the form of a theme with a variation, with the theme then returning, only for Haydn to take us on a slight detour. The chord at the start of bar 90 signals the deviation before we arrive at the conclusion.

As is so often the case in Haydn's compositions, there's a clear sense of fun in this piece. Throughout the movement the syncopated rhythms that we hear right from the start with the tied upbeats provide energy and momentum. The humour is most obvious on the final page, where the pause chord needs careful handling. You might like to slow up slightly on approach to it, although you might equally find it more effective to keep the tempo and create more of a surprise.

Similarly, with the editorial *allargando* marking in bar 105, you could follow this advice (which stems from the arpeggiated chord indications), giving plenty of space to this final statement of the opening theme, or equally ignore it, keeping the same tempo and sweeping all the way to the end with a clear sense of bravura. The same could be said of the editiorial dynamics – there is plenty of space for you to create your own interpretation.

Do have a listen to the whole sonata so you can hear this movement in context. Try to find at least two recordings, so you can compare different approaches. You might also like to listen to a performance on a pianoforte, to give you some idea of the sound Haydn himself would have heard when composing and playing.

- Classical
- Phrasing
- Ornamentation

Marianne Martines led a remarkable life, with the poet Metastasio overseeing much of her education and the composer Joseph Haydn numbering among her neighbours.

Martines was renowned as a singer as well as pianist and composer, and much of her virtuosic singing style can be detected in this flamboyant movement. The score contains plenty of detailed performance markings, and following these will provide plenty of life and energy. In addition, you might like to think about the phrase structures in this piece, and particularly her tendency to repeat a rhythmic and melodic idea, but heightening the effect the second time. Take, for example, bars 22–23 as a simple example. Or the opening 8 bars, where the repetition is melodically decorated, harmonically filled-out and the melody subject to octave transposition. You might like to try to find further examples of this in the piece, almost like doing some detective work to understand how the composer put the music together in the first place.

You might also like to listen to some of Marianne Martines' other compositions as part of your exploration of her style, which include a keyboard concerto and numerous choral and vocal works.

Prelude no. 8 (in G major) / Bullard   Page 18

- Changing time signatures
- Cross-staff notation
- Clef changes in both hands

'Prelude no. 8' comes from a set of piano preludes composed in 2017 by British composer Alan Bullard. This cycle moves through all the major keys, so he composed a second set in 2020 using all the minor keys! Like most piano preludes, this piece shows off the abilities of the instrument, while focusing on a particular mood and set of techniques.

'Prelude no. 8' has a bright and celebratory mood. Loud passages, where chords move down in the right hand, could be a fanfare, while softer sections are lighter but full of suppressed energy. These two styles work in dialogue with each other, orientating towards jubilant statements.

The chopping and changing between different time signatures might look initially intense on the page, but these work naturally, whilst also creating an unpredictable rhythm for the audience that adds to the energy. The grand sweep in bar 41 indicates a freer tempo and you will likely want to take a generous amount of time, playing with the audience's expectations as to when the actual end is.

To explore further you could look at other preludes by Bullard from the major or minor collections, as they cover various styles and moods. Performances of them by the composer can be accessed via his website.

- Melody and accompaniment
- Expressive lines
- Broken chords between both hands

'Mélodie' is the second piece in the set *Trois Mélodies*, written in 1847 by Fanny Hensel, a German composer and pianist from the Romantic era. She was named Fanny Mendelssohn before her marriage and is the sister of Felix Mendelssohn.

This Romantic piece is full of expression. The melody sits on top of the accompaniment, which is shared between both hands. As the title suggests, the melody is the most important element, and it might find it helpful to practise playing the melody and accompaniment separately to support the breathing of these phrases.

The pedalling can be used to help build the swell of each phrase, creating a full-bodied sound, without becoming too muddy. Slight differences in tempo can significantly affect the tone of this piece. You might choose a faster tempo that could bring more urgency, while a slower tempo might create a more melancholy effect. There is also an opportunity to relax the tempo towards the end of phrases and push it slightly in the beginning of some phrases, creating a natural ebb-and-flow. It is a good idea to discuss these issues with your teacher.

Listening to different recordings will help you to settle on your own approach to tempo and dynamics. The performer might want to listen and play through the other two Mélodies in this set, as well as other works by Hensel.

Lento / Fibich   Page 24

- Romantic
- Rich chords in both hands
- Expressive phrasing

Zdeněk Fibich was an overlooked Czech composer, contemporary with Smetana and Dvořák. *Moods, Impressions and Souvenirs* comprises 376 piano miniatures written between 1895 and 1896.

'Lento' has a romantic, yearning atmosphere in-line with the context in which it was written. To create an expressive mood, you could approach the tempo liberally in places, emphasising the emotional weight and intensity of this short piece. The score indicates that the grace notes in, for example, bar 8 come before the beat, but there is some flexibility as to the speed here. These ornaments are therefore distinguished slightly from the broken chord in bar 9, which starts on the beat. In contrast, you might use the grace notes in bar 4 to keep up the momentum, pushing towards the end of the phrase.

Dynamics work closely alongside tempo control. The score does not specify dynamics following *crescendos* and *diminuendos*, but these can be generous, adding significantly to the expression and the impression of deep breaths.

You could listen to different recordings of 'Lento' and other pieces by Fibich. Doing so will help you decide on tempo, dynamics and articulation, although you can also discuss these with your teacher.

Improvisation / MacDowell Page 26

▶ Romantic
▶ Arpeggios
▶ Expression

This evocative miniature by American composer Edward MacDowell reflects his musical training in Europe and shares similarities with the piano music of Gabriel Fauré and Claude Debussy (who attended the Paris conservatoire at the same time as MacDowell) in its expressive qualities and improvisatory mood. This impressionistic piece suggests the composer sitting at his piano and spontaneously pouring out his emotions in an elegant stream of notes. This technically and artistically challenging piece will suit a confident student who enjoys highly expressive music.

The piece contains great dynamic and rhythmic contrasts, but at its heart is a beautiful lyrical melody conveyed with heartfelt expression. A relaxed *Andantino* will enable you to manage the trills, left-hand arpeggios and other figurations. Good arpeggio fingering is essential for the left-hand part, coupled with a flexible mobile wrist to sweep the arm and hand up the keyboard.

To highlight the right-hand melody, practise the top notes separately, but using the fingering you would for the entire chord. This will help with voicing the chords when you add the lower notes back in. The arpeggiated chords should be enjoyed, rather than rushed – the atmosphere of this piece is languorous, its tempo supple but restrained. Use fluid gestures in your playing to enhance the flowing character of the piece.

Assez moderé / Poulenc Page 30

▶ 20th century
▶ Ostinato bass
▶ Lateral movement

Composed in 1918 when Francis Poulenc was just 19, this is the first of a suite of three perpetual movement pieces, and is one of the composer's most popular works. Its mood is generally light-hearted, though the piece ends unresolvedly. Starting in the major key, the music soon slips into the minor mode and grows more chromatic, which creates a very different atmosphere. Poulenc regarded the music as 'easy' and compared it to a brisk stroll by the river Seine in Paris.

A charmingly simple right-hand melody moves through 'right' and 'wrong' keys over a relentless ostinato in the left hand. Good lateral movement in both hands is required to manage the intervals, in particular octaves and ninths. Some changes of finger on a single note are necessary in the right hand to ensure the melody is as *legato* as possible; sparse pedalling will help here too, but be careful not to blur the notes.

This piece benefits from a dry, clean sound. As directed by the composer, the left hand should be played 'without nuance'. This drives the perpetual motion of the piece and as such can roll along evenly underneath the treble. Poulenc is quite specific in his dynamic and expressive markings (for example at bar 14) and much of the character of this

piece derives from the shifting harmonic language and chromaticism rather than gradations in dynamics. The final bar should feel unresolved and ambiguous, the notes washed by the pedal.

Struttin' at the Waldorf / Lane Page 32

▶ Jazz-inspired
▶ Syncopation and cross-rhythms
▶ Sophisticated chords

Philip Lane is best known as a composer of light music, but he also has a special interest in classic cinema. This self-confident, stylish piece recalls the film *Top Hat*, starring Fred Astaire, the glitter and glamour of the Waldorf Hotel in New York in the 1930s, and the orchestration of a big band jazz ensemble.

Infused with jazz rhythms and harmonies, the music has an appealing swagger and plenty of scope for characterisation to highlight its cinematic narrative. Underpinned by a walking left-hand accompaniment suggesting a plucked double bass, the right-hand dotted chords should be relaxed into a triplet crotchet-and-quaver grouping to emphasise the swing of the music; a soft wrist and hand will help to achieve this.

Don't rush the three-against-two rhythms in bars 5, 43, 45 and 46 – if anything, a little rubato here will add to the character – and observe the slur markings. The right hand has to negotiate some sophisticated chords, but in most instances, only one note changes in a progression, allowing the hand to remain in the same position – for example, in bars 2 and 5. While it may be tempting to voice the chords to highlight the melody, all the notes are significant, providing texture and colour.

A cheeky surprise awaits performer and audience from bar 25 with a sequence of *staccato* chords in the high treble suggesting an imaginary tap dance. Keep these chords light and crisp and strictly in time. This section closes with a dramatic descending *glissando* (use the thumbnail to skim across the keys and don't press too hard) before a bridging section which could be a clarinet or saxophone solo, and a reprise of the opening section.

At Miss Florence's / Earl Page 34

▶ Contemporary romantic
▶ Voicing
▶ Expression

The 'Miss Florence' of the title was an old-fashioned schoolteacher, fair but strict, and the piece comes from a suite called *Scenes from Childhood*, a homage to Robert Schumann, who also wrote a suite for children of the same name (*Kinderszenen* in German). David Earl's richly-textured score is reminiscent of Schumann's writing, in particular 'Träumerei' and 'Am Camin', and even quotes from his 'Introduction and allegro appassionato' op. 92 in bars 4-5.

The piece is a kind of Song Without Words, with a treble melody and a muted but textural accompaniment. The challenge here is to highlight and balance the melody with a clear cantabile sound over an accompaniment that is partly taken by the same hand. One way to achieve this would be to practise the upper notes alone, adding the lower notes once the melody is clearly known. Take note of the phrasing and breathe as a singer would as this will allow you to shape the melody naturally – it may even help you to sing the melody out loud as you practise it.

The piece is highly expressive, despite the marking semplice ('simply') and the unexpected, Schumannesque shifts in harmony lend a strongly romantic character to the music. Use the pedal almost continuously with careful changes on each new harmony; in some instances finger pedal will serve the music better to avoid blurring the sounds, for example, in the left-hand upper voice in bars 4–6. Fluctuations in tempo suggest rubato and you should feel free to experiment further with this to increase the expressiveness of the music.

Soho / Botterill — Page 36

▶ Varying musical styles
▶ Rhythm and meter
▶ Expression

Charlotte Botterill is a British composer and her piece 'Soho' reflects her eclectic approach to composing. It features several contemporary musical styles, including pop and soul, as well as a strong jazz influence. An evocative snapshot of the varied and edgy nightlife of the Soho district of London – from cool cafés and cocktail bars to jazz clubs – this piece is an atmospheric 'sound journey' through the night-time streets, and will appeal to older teenagers and adult players who are confident with syncopation and changing metres.

Much of the character of the music comes from swung rhythms, syncopations and cross-rhythms, its muted jazz harmonies, and repeating motifs, or fragments of motifs, such as the right-hand pattern of chords in bar 4 and the bass riff and groove of bars 4–10, which is the main melodic focus of the first section. There is plenty of scope for thoughtful rubato and expression in the first section, while bars 22–38 should follow a strict beat.

The composer has indicated only sparse pedal markings, giving you the option to try out additional pedalling ideas to create colour and mood in the music; some sections may benefit from richer pedalling. The final tempo change offers scope for a really atmospheric ending, with the pedal slightly blurring the closing notes.

Subtle changes in dynamics, for example in the bass riff and the recurring chord groove in bars 7 and 10, will lend greater expression and atmosphere to the music. Don't be afraid to experiment with shifts in dynamics, and play boldly and with attitude through the *mf* and *f* sections.

Authors: Martin Ford, Owen Barton and Frances Wilson

Invention no. 12 in A major

BWV 783

Johann Sebastian Bach
(1685-1750)

Capriccio in G minor

HWV 483

George Frideric Handel
(1685-1759)

Finale

3rd movt from *Sonata in D major*, Hob XVI:24

Joseph Haydn
(1732-1809)

* All dynamics in this piece are editorial and may be seen as a suggestion only.

Omit the repeats in the exam.

Allegro

1st movt from *Sonata in E major*

Marianne Martines
(1744–1812)

Omit the repeats in the exam.

Prelude no. 8 (in G major)

Alan Bullard
(b. 1947)

Published by Colne Edition (www.colneedition.co.uk), sole selling agents Spartan Press Ltd. (www.spartanpress.co.uk)

Mélodie

op. 4 no. 2

Fanny Hensel
(1805-1847)

[Blank page to facilitate page turns]

Lento

no. 139 from *Moods, Impressions and Souvenirs*, op. 41

Zdeněk Fibich
(1850–1900)

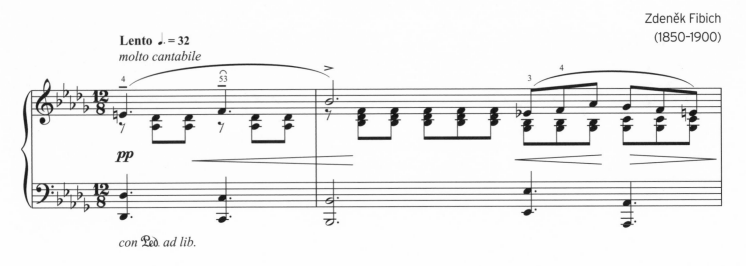

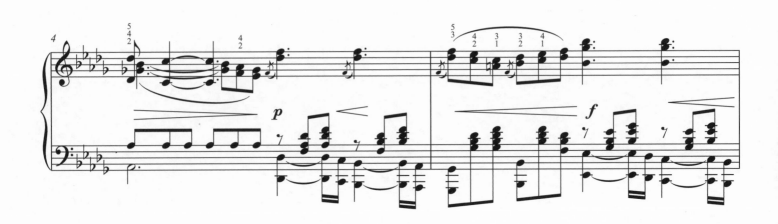

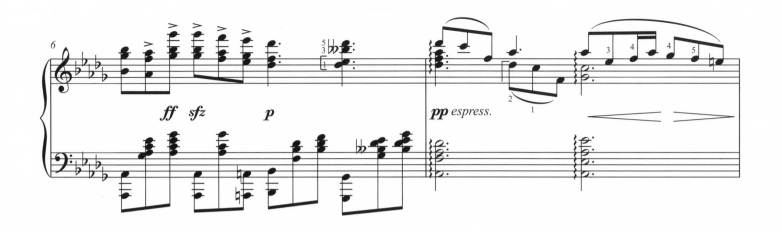

Improvisation

no. 4 from *Twelve Virtuoso Studies*, op. 46

Edward MacDowell
(1860–1908)

* Consider starting this trill very slowly and gradually increasing the speed.

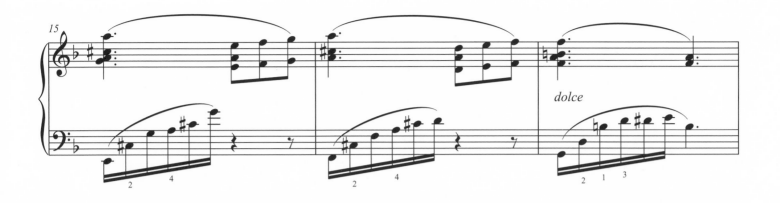

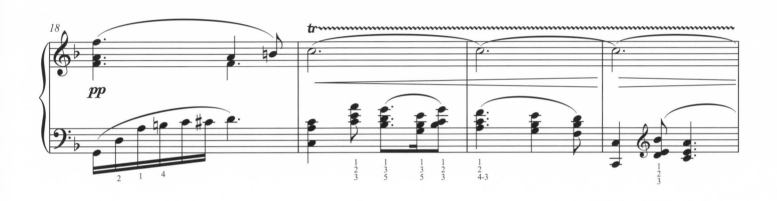

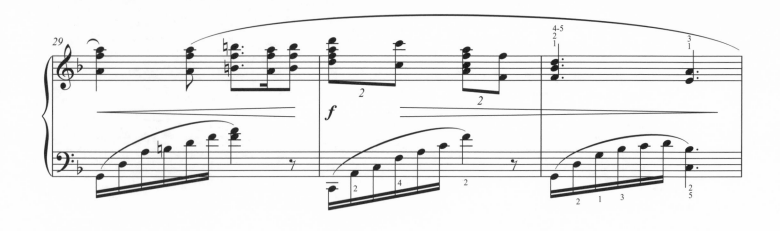

[Blank page to facilitate page turns]

Assez modéré

no. 1 from *Trois mouvements perpétuels*

Francis Poulenc
(1899–1963)

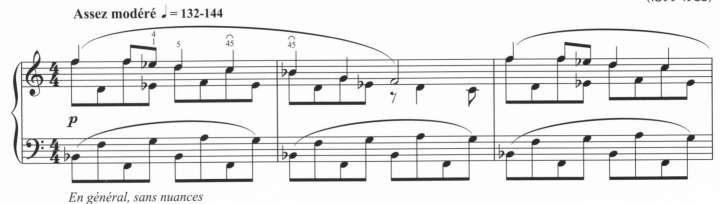

En général, sans nuances

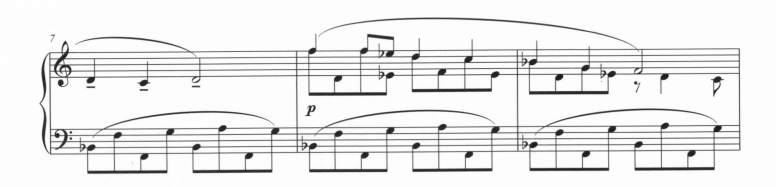

Play the repeat in the exam.

30   Composer's metronome mark ♩ = 144

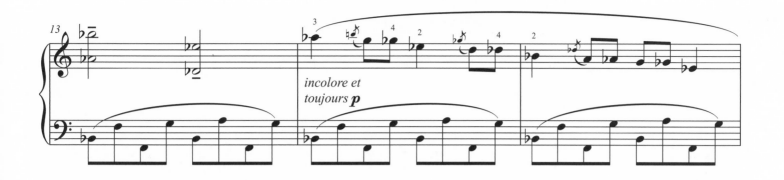

incolore et
toujours **p**

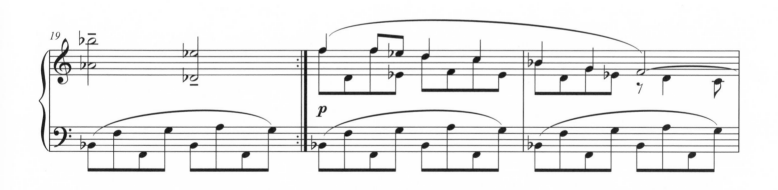

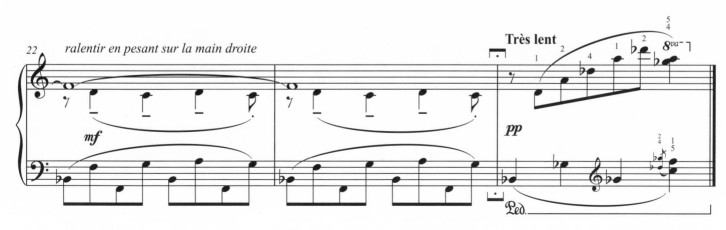

ralentir en pesant sur la main droite

Très lent

Struttin' at the Waldorf

no. 3 from *Three Little Bites at the Big Apple*

Philip Lane
(b. 1950)

* A picture of Fred Astaire gliding through the lobby of the
New York hotel around 1935, in top hat, white tie and tails.

(imaginary tap dance steps)

* Players with smaller hands may omit the lower C.

At Miss Florence's

(homage to Robert Schumann)

David Earl
(b. 1951)

34

Soho

Charlotte Botterill
(b. 1989)

Exercises

1a. A Lazy Summer's Day – tone, balance and voicing

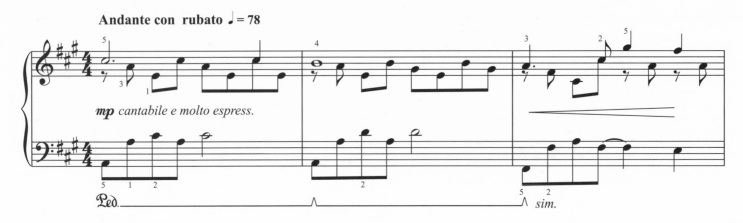

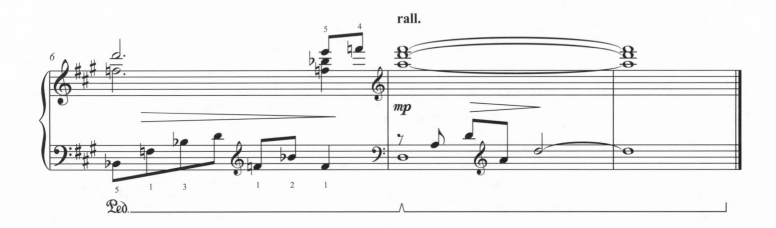

1b. Pensive – tone, balance and voicing

2a. Raindrops – co-ordination

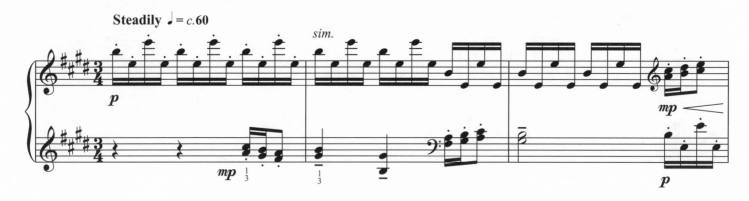

2b. The Clifftop Citadel – co-ordination

Allegro maestoso ♩ = 132

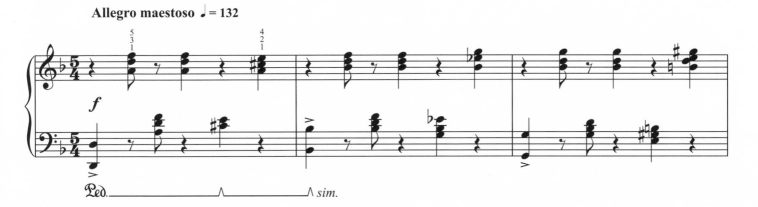

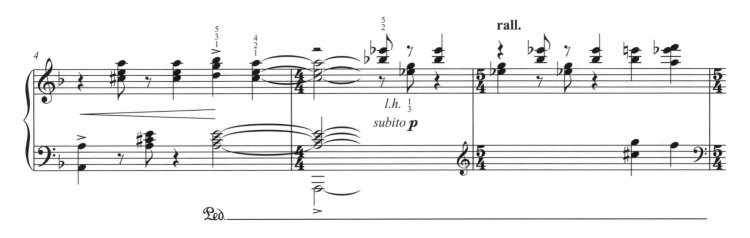

43

3a. Interrupted Arabesque – finger & wrist strength and flexibility

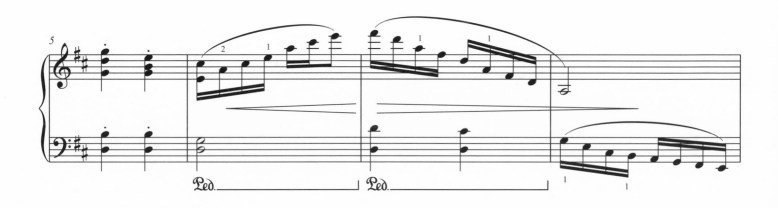

3b. Go for Baroque – finger & wrist strength and flexibility